Mystery Mob
and the
Scary Santa

Roger Hurn

Illustrated by
Stik

RISING★STARS

Rising Stars UK Ltd.
7 Hatchers Mews, Bermondsey Street, London SE1 3GS
www.risingstars-uk.com

The right of Roger Hurn to be identified as the author of this work
has been asserted by him in accordance with the Copyright,
Design and Patents Act 1988.

Published 2008
Reprinted 2014

Text, design and layout © Rising Stars UK Ltd.

Cover design: Burville-Riley Partnership
Illustrator: Stik, Bill Greenhead for Illustration Ltd
Text design and typesetting: Andy Wilson
Publisher: Gill Budgell
Editor: Catherine Baker

All rights reserved. No part of this publication may be reproduced,
stored in a retrieval system, or transmitted in any form by any means,
electronic, mechanical, photocopying, recording or otherwise without
the prior permission of Rising Stars UK Ltd.

British Library Cataloguing in Publication Data.
A CIP record for this book is available from the British Library

ISBN: 978-1-84680-427-4

Printed in the UK by Ashford Colour Press Ltd.

MIX
Paper from
responsible sources
FSC® C011748

Contents

Meet the Mystery Mob

Name:

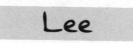

FYI: Gummy hasn't got much brain – and even fewer teeth.

Loves: Soup.

Hates: Toffee chews.

Fact: The brightest thing about him is his shirt.

Name:

Lee

FYI: If Lee was any cooler he'd be a cucumber.

Loves: Hip-hop.

Hates: Hopscotch.

Fact: He has his own designer label (which he peeled off a tin).

Leabharlanna Poiblí Chathair Baile Átha Cliath
Dublin City Public Libraries

Name:

Rob

FYI: Rob lives in his own world – he's just visiting planet Earth.

Loves: Daydreaming.

Hates: Nightmares.

Fact: Rob always does his homework – he just forgets to write it down.

Name:

Dwayne

FYI: Dwayne is smarter than a tree full of owls.

Loves: Anything complicated.

Hates: Join-the-dots books.

Fact: If he was any brighter you could use him as a floodlight at football matches.

Name:

Chet

FYI: Chet is as brave as a lion with steel jaws.

Loves: Having adventures.

Hates: Knitting.

Fact: He's as tough as the chicken his granny cooks for his tea.

Name:

Adi

FYI: Adi is as happy as a football fan with tickets to the big match.

Loves: Telling jokes.

Hates: Moaning minnies.

Fact: He knows more jokes than a jumbo joke book.

Christmas Crackers

Christmas is coming. Rob and Lee
are taking Lee's little brother, Dirk,
to see Father Christmas at
the Costa Fortune Department Store.

Lee   Dirk's really excited about going
to see Father Christmas,
aren't you, Dirk?

Dirk nods his head and grins.

Rob   Hey, Dirk, do you know who
            gives presents and bites people?
            It's Santa Jaws!

Dirk stops grinning and bursts into tears.

Dirk   Don't wanna see Santa Jaws!

Lee   Oh, thanks a bunch, Rob.
It's all right, Dirk. We're going
to see a nice Santa Claus –
not a shark.

Rob   Sorry, Dirk.

Dirk holds Lee's hand and glares at Rob.

Lee   (sighing) And talking of presents
            – what are you getting Adi
            for Christmas?

Rob   A big box of Christmas crackers –
            he needs some new jokes!

Lee   But the jokes in Christmas
            crackers are sooo corny.

Rob   That's why they'll be just right
            for Adi!

Lee   Okay. So what are you getting
            for Chet?

Rob   Well, he likes to think he's
James Bond, so I'm buying him
some mince spies.

Lee   Great – but you'd better
keep them undercover.

Rob   You got it. What are you buying
for Gummy?

Lee   I've got him a King Wenceslas
pizza.

Rob   What's that?

Lee   A pizza that's deep and crisp and even.

Rob   Awesome. What about Dwayne?

Lee   Well, Dwayne's into reading big time, so I've got him a Christmas alphabet.

Rob   What's a Christmas alphabet?

Lee   It's like a normal alphabet, but it's got No-el in it.

Rob   He'll love it.

Lee   Yeah, but not half as much
as Dirk's going to love
Santa's grotto. It's even got Elfvis,
the rock 'n' roll elf.

Rob   Wow, he's as cool as an iceberg
with chilli sauce. I want to
see him!

Lee   Okay, but I want to check out
the sports department first.
They've got some killer new
football boots.

Rob   So?

Lee So I need to show you which ones I want for my Christmas present from you.

Rob You're Christmas crackers! I can't afford fancy football boots!

Lee Scrooge!

Rob I'm not! I said I can't afford the boots. But I'm happy to buy you the laces.

Who Ate All
the Mince Pies?

It's quite late by the time Rob, Lee
and Dirk arrive at the grotto.
They are the only ones there.

Lee   Phew! We made it just in time.

Rob I don't know about that.
Nothing's stirring in the grotto –
not even a mouse.

Lee Hmmm … that's odd.

Rob Well, let's go inside.
Maybe Santa's having
a tea break.

Lee Hang on. It sounds like someone
in the grotto's yelling for help.

Rob   No, it can't be. Unless one of
the elves has trodden on a piece
of holly.

Lee   Or maybe Santa's got stuck
in the chimney.

Rob   That'll be it. He's eaten
too many mince pies.

Lee   Yeah, Santa needs to go
on a diet.

17

Rob   Hey, do you know how Frosty the Snowman loses weight?

Lee   No.

Rob   He goes sunbathing.

Lee   Very funny, Rob. But Dirk still wants to see Father Christmas, so what are we going to do?

Rob   I don't know. It's all gone
           very quiet in the grotto.

Dirk starts to sniffle. He's about to
cry again.

Lee   True, but I think it's going
           to get very noisy out here
           if we don't see Santa soon.

Rob   Okay, but aren't we supposed
to wait for Elfvis the Elf
to take us in?

Lee   Yeah, but it looks like Elfvis
has left the grotto. Anyway,
there's no point in us
hanging around like spare
Christmas decorations.
Let's go in.

The Grotty Grotto

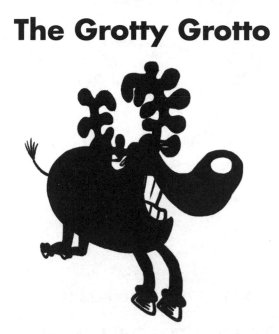

It's quite dark in the grotto. Someone has switched the fairy lights off. There is no sign of Elfvis or Santa.

Rob I wonder who was making that noise just now?

Lee Search me. Hey, someone's taken the red light bulb out of Rudolph's nose.

21

Rob   Why would they do that?

Lee   Either they don't like life-sized model reindeer, or they wanted to make it even darker in here.

Rob   I don't like it. This grotto's making me shiver.

Lee   That'll be all the fake snow.

Rob   No, it's 'cos it's creepy.

Lee   Yeah, this is one grotty grotto.

Rob   Hey, I can hear someone
moving about in Santa's
Magic Toyshop.

Lee   You're right!

Dirk   I wanna see Santa.

Rob   No, I think we'll give Santa
a miss.

Lee   Yeah, sorry, Dirk.

Dirk   (yelling) I WANNA SEE SANTA!

Rob   Argggh! My ears!

Lee   Okay, Dirk. We'll go
and see Santa.

Lee opens the door to Santa's
Magic Toyshop. He sees a very
scary-looking Santa with a big sack
of toys.

Santa   (gruffly) What do you want?

Rob   We want to see Santa.

Santa   All right. You've seen me.

Lee   Wait a minute. Where are all the elves?

Santa   (grumpily) At the North Pole. Now hop it.

Leabharlanna Poibli Chathair Baile Átha Cliath
Dublin City Public Libraries

Rob	Hey, aren't you going to ask Dirk if he's been a good boy?
Lee	And what he wants for Christmas?
Rob	And then give him a toy from your sack?
Lee	And then wish him a Merry Christmas and say 'Ho ho ho'?
Rob	'Cos that's what Santas do.

The Santa reaches into his sack.
He pulls out a doll and throws it to Dirk.

Santa   There you are. Merry Christmas.
Ho ho ho off.

Dirk   I don't wanna doll.

Lee   Yes, you do. Come on guys,
we're outta here.

Rob and Lee drag Dirk and his doll
out of Santa's Magic Toyshop.

The Wishing Well

Lee's mum is waiting for them outside the grotto.

Mum Hey, I like your doll, Dirk!

Dirk (slyly) I got it for you, Mummy.

Mum Oh Dirky, you're such a good boy. Come on. Mummy's going to buy you an ice cream in the café.

Dirk winks at Lee and Rob and goes off to the café with his mum.

Rob   I don't like that Santa.

Lee   Me neither. He's a fake!

Rob   But what's he up to?

Lee   There's only one way to find out.

The boys sneak back to the grotto.
They see a pair of fur boots sticking up
from out of the wishing well.

Rob   Who's that?

Lee   I don't know. Let's grab
a boot each and pull him out.

Rob   Yikes! He weighs a ton.

Lee   Wow! It's Father Christmas.

Rob   Hey, Santa's meant to go down
chimneys, not wishing wells.

Lee   Yeah, but someone's tied him up.
They must have pushed him in.

Rob   Who did this to you, Santa?

Santa   Grrrwpphfff.

Rob   Ha! I guess that's the name of an evil goblin.

Lee   Duh! No, it's not. Santa can't talk. He's got a gag in his mouth.

Rob   Whoops! Sorry, Santa.

Rob unties the gag.

Santa   Thank goodness you've found me.
A crook dressed up in
a Santa costume is stealing
all the Christmas presents
from my Magic Toyshop.
They're for the kids
at the local hospital.

Lee   Don't you worry about him,
Santa. You go and get the cops.

Rob   That's right. Leave the scary
Santa to us. We'll fix him!

Santa Gets the Sack

Rob and Lee dash back into the grotto.
They bump into the Scary Santa!
He's coming out of the Magic Toyshop.

Scary Santa

Get out of my way.

Lee   No way. You're not the real
Santa.

Scary Santa

Wise up, kid. There isn't
a real Santa.

Rob   Yes there is. And you're stealing
his sack of toys.

Lee   So put it back in the Magic
Toyshop right now!

Scary Santa

No chance. I've got
a sackful of toys to deliver
on Christmas Eve – but not
to sick kids! Ha ha ha.

Rob You've got that wrong.
It's 'Ho ho ho', not 'Ha ha ha'.

Scary Santa

Whatever. Now I'm going to lock
you two in the Magic Toyshop.
Move it!

Lee sees a football on the ground.
He grabs it and kicks it hard
at the Scary Santa. It hits him right
in the middle of his large belly.

Scary Santa

Ooooffff!

The Scary Santa falls backwards
and lands on the life-sized model
of Rudolph the Red-nosed Reindeer.

Rob   Great shot, Lee.
          You've sent him flying.

Lee   And he's landed on Rudolph.

Rob   Wow! He's sat on Rudolph's
          start button. But he's way too big
          for the reindeer ride. Rudolph's
          going mad. He's like a bucking
          bronco – not a reindeer.

Lee   Yeah, the Scary Santa looks really scared.

Rob   Too right! He's hanging on for rein-deer life – geddit?!

Scary Santa
         Help!

Lee   Awesome! Rudolph's going faster and faster!

Rudolph gives one last kick. Scary Santa flies off and crashes head first into the model of Frosty the Snowman.

Rob   Hey, the Scary Santa's out cold.
          But I guess that's what happens
          when you get hit by a snowman.

Lee   Frosty did say 'freeze',
          but Scary Santa didn't listen.

Rob   Now we can give the sack of toys
          to the real Santa.

Lee   And he can take it to the kids
          in the hospital.

Rob   While the cops put Scary Santa
          in the cooler.

Lee   I guess
          you can say
          he got the sack
          for trying
          to get the sack!

Leabharlanna Poiblí Chathair Baile Átha Cliath
Dublin City Public Libraries

About the author

Roger Hurn has:

 had a hit record in Turkey

 won *The Weakest Link* on TV

swum with sharks on the
Great Barrier Reef.

Now he's a writer, and he hopes you like
reading about the Mystery Mob as much as he
likes writing about them.

Christmas quiz

Questions

1 Who beats his chest and swings from Christmas cake to Christmas cake?

2 What do snowmen eat for breakfast?

3 What is Santa Claus' dog called?

4 What happens if you eat the Christmas decorations?

5 Why are Christmas trees like bad knitters?

6 What do you get if you cross an apple with a Christmas tree?

7 How long should a reindeer's legs be?

8 What do snowmen ride?

Answers

1 Tarzipan!
2 Snowflakes!
3 Santa Paws!
4 You get tinsel-itus!
5 They both drop their needles!
6 A pineapple!
7 Just long enough to reach the ground!
8 Icecycles!

How did you score?

- If you got all eight Christmas quiz answers correct, then you are the star on the top of the Christmas tree.

- If you got six Christmas quiz answers correct, then you're a real Christmas cracker!

- If you got fewer than four Christmas answers correct, then Santa Claus may not be coming to your town.

When I was a kid

Question Did you like Christmas when you were a kid?

Roger Yes. My favourite part after opening the presents was Christmas dinner.

Question So did you eat turkey?

Roger I did, but everyone in my family liked the turkey drumsticks best so there were never enough turkey legs for us all.

Question So what did you do?

Roger Well, my dad was a farmer so he bred a turkey with six legs.

Question Wow! What did it taste like?

Roger I don't know.

Question Why not?

Roger Because he could never catch it!

Adi's favourite Christmas joke

What do you get if you cross Father Christmas with a detective?

Santa Clues!

How to have a cracker of a Christmas

 Remember, Christmas is about giving as well as getting. It's amazing how making someone else happy at Christmas makes you feel happy too.

 Send Father Christmas a letter – to Father Christmas, North Pole, SAN TA1. You'll get a reply, but he still might not bring you all the things you've asked for!

 Make your own Christmas cards for your family. Your mum, aunties and gran will like them much better than shop-bought ones – and you'll save money!

Make up your own Christmas quiz for all the family to play after you've had your Christmas dinner. It'll be lots more fun than watching some boring old movie on TV.

 Feed the birds. Christmas can be hard for birds as there's not much food about for them. So hang up a stocking full of bird food in your garden on Christmas Day. You'll have lots of fun watching them tucking into their Christmas dinner – only don't tell them what you had!

Five fantastic Christmas facts

1   Apart from Rudolph, Santa has eight more reindeer. They are called: Dasher, Dancer, Prancer, Vixen, Comet, Cupid, Donner and Blitzen. He must be really heavy if he needs all those reindeer to pull his sleigh!

2   Only female reindeer keep their antlers in winter. This means every single one of Santa's reindeer – including Rudolph – is a girl!

3   The first Christmas puddings were actually a kind of thick porridge with raisins and wine in it. Hmmm … sounds tasty!

4   People ate goose on Christmas Day in England until Henry the Eighth decided he preferred turkey. But then Henry always did like to 'gobble' up his food!

5   A killjoy called Oliver Cromwell banned Christmas for everyone in England from 1647 to 1660. Maybe he was just too mean to buy Christmas presents!

Christmas lingo

Carol A Christmas song celebrating
the birth of Jesus, not the name of Santa's wife.

Grotto A man-made cave or cavern where
young children go to see Father Christmas.
It's not a rotten game of Lotto.

Kriss Kringle This is the German name
for Santa Claus. Mind you, if the chimney
is too hot, he'll be burnt to a Krisp Kringle.

Sleigh The cart Santa Claus uses on Christmas
Eve. When the reindeer tell a joke they say:
'This one will sleigh you.' Slay you – geddit?!!

Stocking The long sock you hang up
on Christmas Eve so that Santa can put
your presents in it. If you haven't got a stocking
then use a pillow case, not a pair of your
mum's tights!

Yule The old word for Christmas time. If Santa
finds out you've been naughty – Yule be sorry!

Mystery Mob

Mystery Mob Set 1:

Mystery Mob and the Abominable Snowman
Mystery Mob and the Big Match
Mystery Mob and the Circus of Doom
Mystery Mob and the Creepy Castle
Mystery Mob and the Haunted Attic
Mystery Mob and the Hidden Treasure
Mystery Mob and the Magic Bottle
Mystery Mob and the Missing Millions
Mystery Mob and the Monster on the Moor
Mystery Mob and the Mummy's Curse
Mystery Mob and the Time Machine
Mystery Mob and the UFO

Mystery Mob Set 2:

Mystery Mob and the Ghost Town
Mystery Mob and the Bonfire Night Plot
Mystery Mob and the April Fools' Day Joker
Mystery Mob and the Great Pancake Day Race
Mystery Mob and the Scary Santa
Mystery Mob and the Conker Conspiracy
Mystery Mob and the Top Talent Contest
Mystery Mob and the Night in the Waxworks
Mystery Mob and the Runaway Train
Mystery Mob and the Wrong Robot
Mystery Mob and the Day of the Dinosaurs
Mystery Mob and the Man-eating Tiger

RISING ★ STARS

Mystery Mob books are available from most booksellers.

**For mail order information
please call Rising Stars on freephone 0800 091 1602
or visit www.risingstars-uk.com**